pink book

Simple arrangements by Jo McNally for KS2 choirs and easy Piano/Keyboard accompaniment

plus CD demonstration

Novello Publishing Limited
8/9 Frith Street
London W1D 3JB

Order No. NOV072521

Welcome to the Novello Junior Choral Club!

This is a series of choral packets with photocopiable parts for your singers, in association with the British Federation of Young Choirs.

The series is intended for beginner KS2 choirs and their teacher/conductor. The songs are designed to help your choir develop their singing within a range suitable for young voices, reinforce basic score reading skills, encourage good musicianship and develop ensemble skills.

The harmony parts have been kept simple so that your singers will develop their confidence and musicality, and reinforce their reading skills. I think initially at this level it is a good idea to teach by rote with good example singing from the teacher, and then introduce the score. There are photocopiable student sheets for each of the songs. I like my young singers to share copies as 'two heads are better than one' and partners often help each other to develop a sense of ensemble and teamwork.

Remember to give all your students a chance to sing a harmony part, even if it's only in canon. Start early to develop singing inner parts!

The piano/keyboard accompaniments are simple, but effective, and capable of being played by just about anyone! (I know, as I can play them!). This is intentional as I want to encourage you to 'conduct' your group and get out from behind that piano!

There are four songs in this set which could be the major part of a term's work. As time is often limited for young choirs (before school, at lunchtime, after school) and rarely longer than 30 minute sessions per week, this could be your answer to programming challenges.

The main theme for this set of pieces is sight-singing. The pieces include a skill-builder, a folk-song, something pretty (the 'parent pleaser') and an up-tempo jazz piece. In addition there are some extra ideas for vocal development, teaching the songs, and performance.

I hope you and your group will enjoy this series!!

Jo McNally

Exclusive distributors:
Music Sales Limited
Newmarket Road, Bury St Edmunds, Suffolk, IP33 3YB
All rights reserved.

Order No. NOV072521
ISBN 0-7119-8913-3

This book © Copyright 2001 Novello & Company Limited
Cover design and additional text by Miranda Harvey
Music and text set by Note-orious Productions Ltd
Printed in the United Kingdom by Caligraving Limited, Thetford, Norfolk

pink book

Notes for Teachers

1. Before you begin, and throughout your rehearsal, check and reinforce 'good' **posture!** The key is alignment, so that your body helps you sing. Here are the basics which apply whether standing or sitting.

    - stand tall and proud.
    - shoulders should be as wide as possible.
        - too far forward and you look like a penguin.
        - too far back and you're at attention like a soldier.
    - knees not locked, but still supporting the body.
    - face nice and relaxed with eyes open and eager.

2. Take the time to do a **warm-up** with your group. Even a short exercise helps to set the tone for your rehearsal and gets the group thinking together as an ensemble. Start with a stretch. When your group feels comfortable with stretching, add an *n* hum, gradually sliding up and down in small hills of not more than an octave!

    - Arms – alternate each arm and gently reach for a winning 'lottery ticket'.
    - Shoulders – lift both shoulders slowly up to your ears and slowly bring down.
        - stretch them both gently to the back (soldier) and return.
        - stretch them gently to the front (penguin) and return.
    - Head – with a tall, proud head gently turn to the left, then right and return.
    - Eyes – move them up, down, side to side, and then in slow, large circles.
    - Face – anything goes here! How many parts of your face can you move?

3. **Get out from behind that piano!!** Your singers will never watch you and react to your conducting unless you train them to do so! The accompaniments are designed to be simple, but you could ask another teacher to play them or use that memory facility on your electronic keyboard! Try learning all the songs away from the keyboard and use it only as an optional extra. Your singers will quickly learn to listen to each other and begin to develop 'ensemble' skills.

4. You'll notice that these pieces have **no tempo or dynamic markings**. I want you to decide with your choir what works best for your group! Also, this is not great art, so feel free to add or delete where it's appropriate for your circumstances. You might want to use the percussion facility on one of your keyboards as an accompaniment to enhance a song. Why not!

5. **No high and low voices!** Everyone needs to be able to use their whole voice. The ranges of these pieces should be singable by anyone, so change around who sings each part. It's the only way singers learn to be comfortable and competent singing inner harmonies.

6. **Singing is supposed to be enjoyable**, not just for your students but for you too!

Rocky Mountain

Rocky Mountain is a folksong in three verses with chorus. This is a great piece for introducing sight-singing skills. Simple rhythm patterns are combined with an extended tonic triad. The descant part imitates the tune using echo and unison, and the harmony is created by extending the duration of the final note of the chorus phrase. To make the piece more interesting each verse changes key, moving from C to D to F.

Teaching Hints

- First teach the song by rote. Sing all the verses in the same key. Enjoy the taste of the words, getting your singers to identify the verse and chorus sections. Then begin to think about the melodic shape of each phrase. Look for these melodic patterns. Start with the key of C.

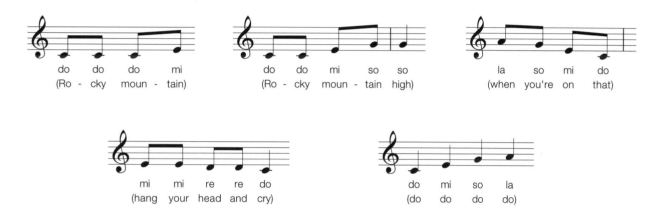

- I find using solfege handsigns particularly useful to reinforce the patterns. I approach key signatures as secret code. When your singers begin to feel confident with the patterns in the key of C, look at the other two keys and begin to notice how the patterns are the same but each written in a new code.

- The gradual key change will begin to help stretch the singing range of your group and extend their sight-singing and score-reading skills. Have the following patterns available on a card to show them side by side and as a reminder.

Skin and Bones

This is one of my favourite spooky songs and I know I'm taking liberties, but I've stretched the 'oo' section to double it's normal length. No excuses really except that I think it gives a more haunting feeling. Watch out for the added sound effects, especially the blood-curdling scream!

Teaching Hints

- First teach the 'oo' section, paying close attention to accurate pitch and tuning.

- Then sing the song without the sound effects, with your students adding the 'oo' section. Sing the verses using a slightly hushed and breathy quality to your tone. Don't forget to make the most of your blood-curdling scream! It will only work once, and then they'll all want to join in.

- Next teach the verses making a difference between the fuller tone of the 'oo' section and the more hushed quality of the verses.

- The sound effects of *spooky breathing, quiet growl* and *evil laugh* should be added last, and are merely a suggestion. Your students may have more interesting sounds to use. You might even want to incorporate a spooky soundscape representing the graveyard, or even worse, the inside of a closet as an introduction to the piece. Enjoy!

All Through the Night

A beautiful tune, simply set with a melodic canon using sequence and repetition.

Teaching Hints

- This is a good opportunity to teach a new rhythm syllable.

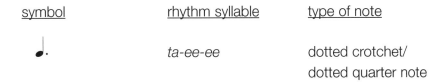

symbol	rhythm syllable	type of note
♩.	*ta-ee-ee*	dotted crotchet/ dotted quarter note

- When teaching the main tune be aware of patterns which move by step or interval.

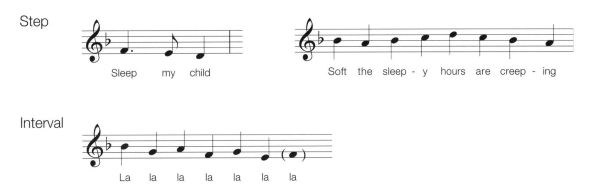

- The 'la' section may prove a bit challenging. Try doubling this section with recorders or tuned percussion.

So-Fa Jazz

So-fa Jazz is a cheerful piece with solfege as the text, and the second verse using treble/G clef note names. The ostinati section is meant to be sung *a cappella*. Sing the tune (accompanied section) first followed in turn by each ostinati phrases then return to the tune, gradually combining the ostinati.

Teaching Hints

- Start with the tune, teach the solfege as text. Make sure that in the semi-breve/whole note phrase the sounds are stretched and the tone is consistent.

- Gradually add the ostinati patterns working from voice parts 1 to 4 which gradually increase in difficulty. Make sure each pattern is sung correctly before attempting to combine them.

- This is a great opportunity for young singers to contribute their own patterns and to write their own tune! Feel free to extend the piece as you choose.

- You might try teaching the piece using the treble/G clef notes as the text, and as the piece is in the key of C major, tuned percussion, recorder, or other instruments could be used to reinforce the ostinati section or improvise over the accompaniment part of the tune.

Rocky Mountain

Traditional American
Arranged by Jo McNally

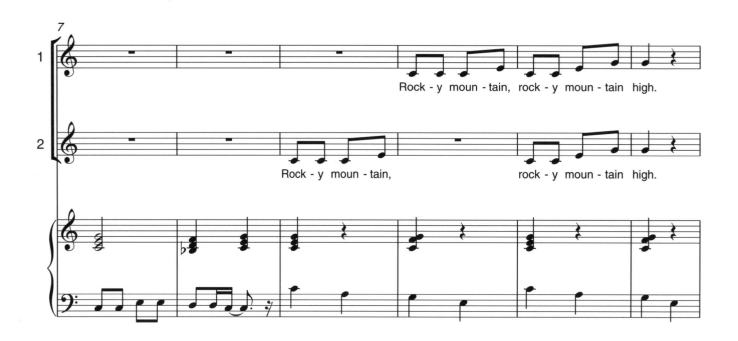

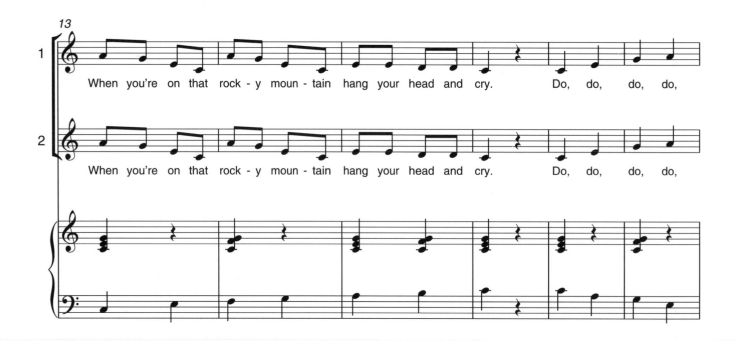

When you're in that sun - ny val - ley sing it soft and low. Do, do, do, do,

When you're in that sun - ny val - ley sing it soft and low. Do, do, do, do,

do._____ Do, do, do, do, do._____

do re - mem - ber me. Do, do, do, do, do re - mem - ber me.

Skin and Bones

Traditional Southern Appalachian Folksong
Arranged by Jo McNally

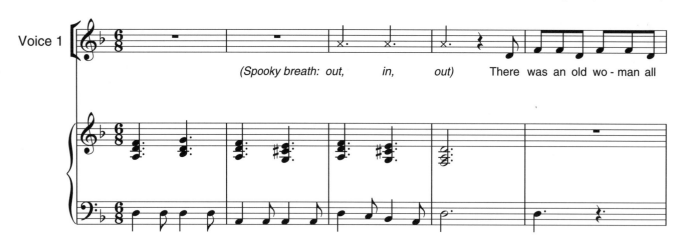

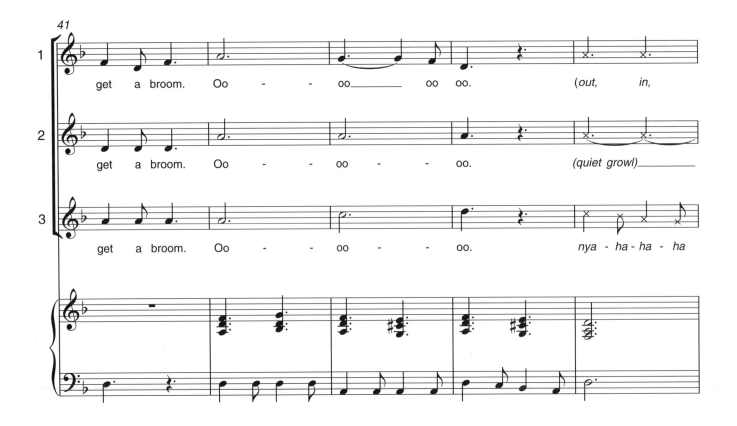

13

All Through the Night

Traditional Welsh Folksong
Arranged by Jo McNally

So-Fa Jazz

Jo McNally

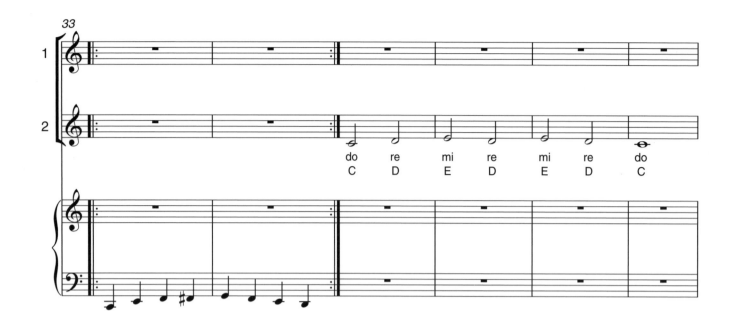

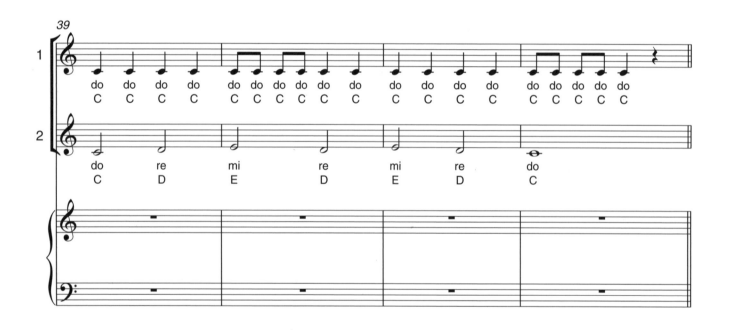

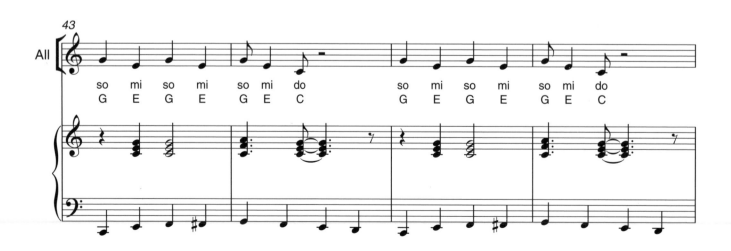

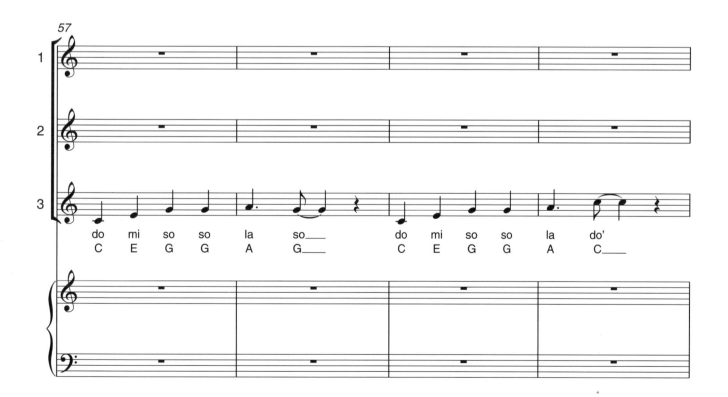

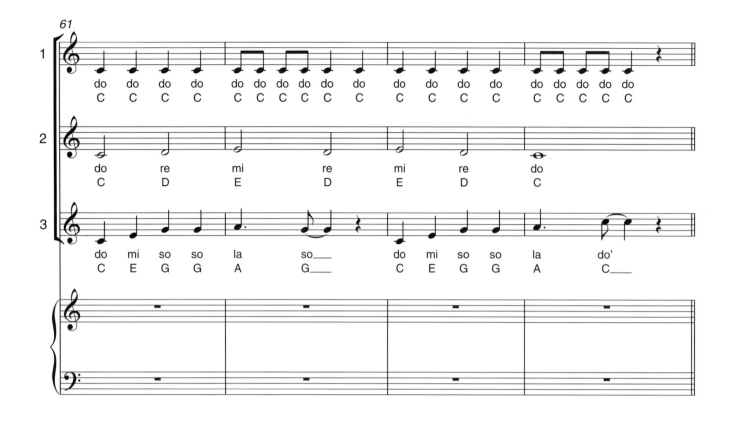

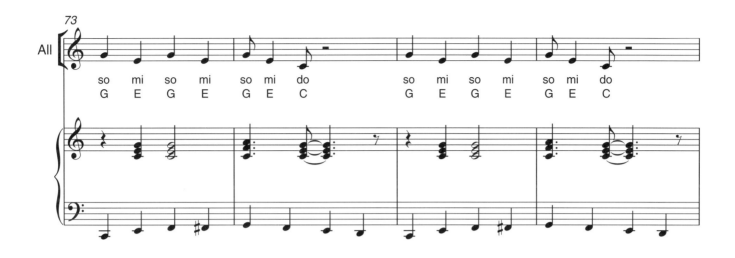

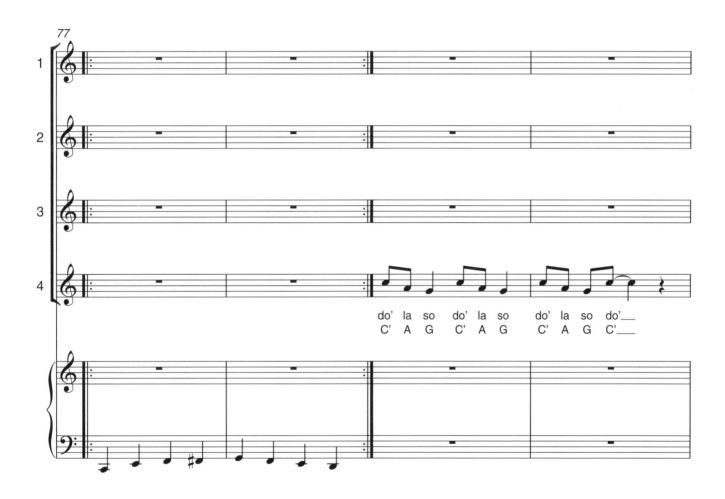

23

Rocky Mountain
(Vocal Part)

Traditional American
Arranged by Jo McNally

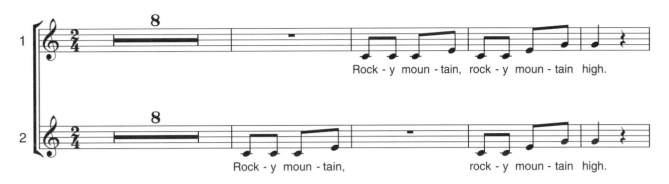

Skin and Bones
(Vocal Part)

Traditional Southern Appalachian Folksong
Arranged by Jo McNally

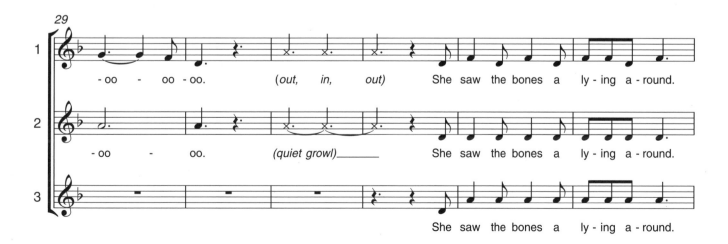

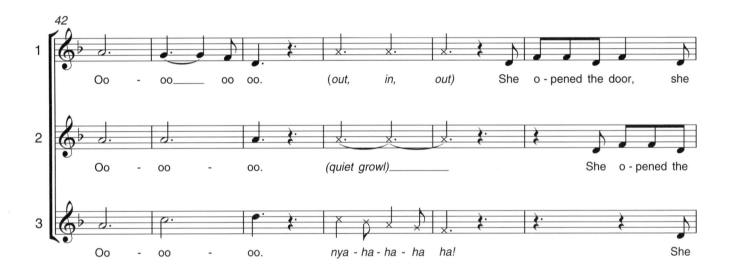

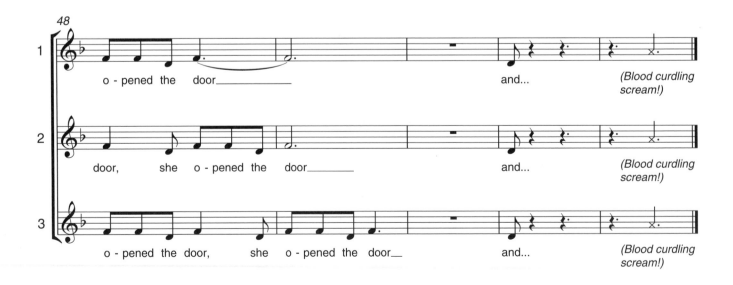

All Through the Night
(Vocal Part)

Traditional Welsh Folksong
Arranged by Jo McNally

19

1: all through the night. La la la la la la la

2: La la la la la la la la la la la la la

23

1: la la la la la la la la la la la la la la la la la la

2: la la la la la la la la la la la la la la la la la la la la

So-fa jazz

Jo McNally

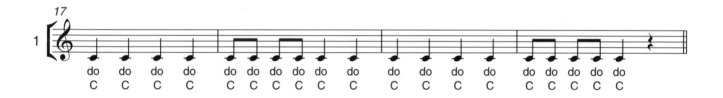

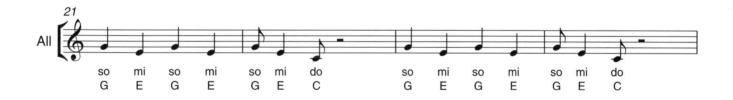

This page may be photocopied

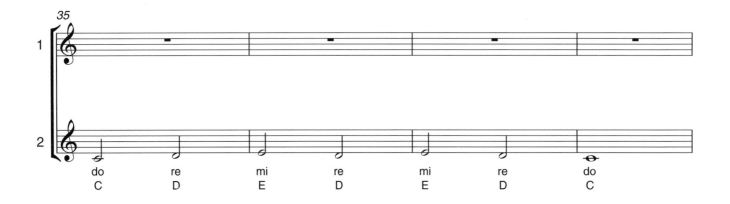

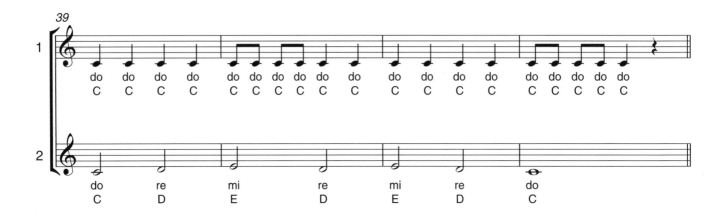

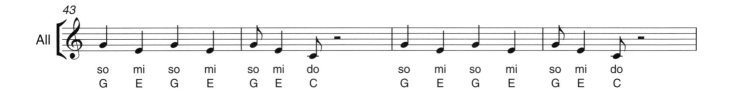

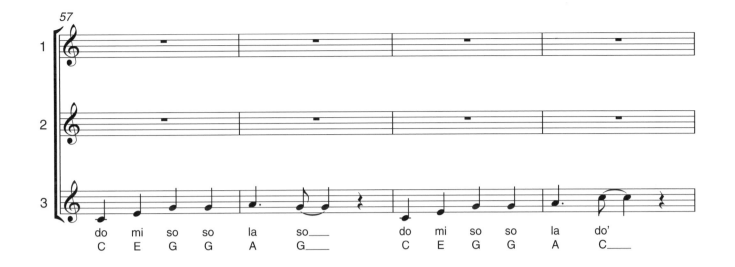

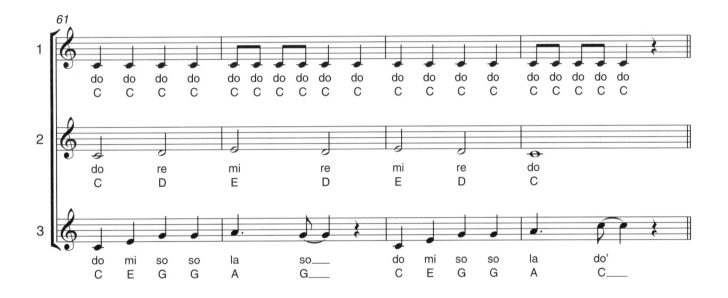

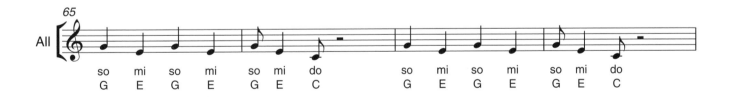

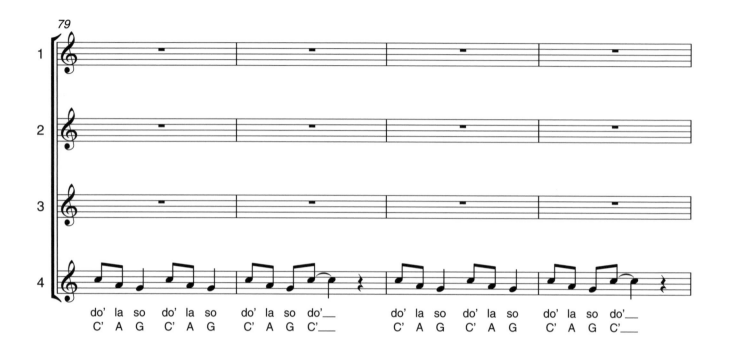

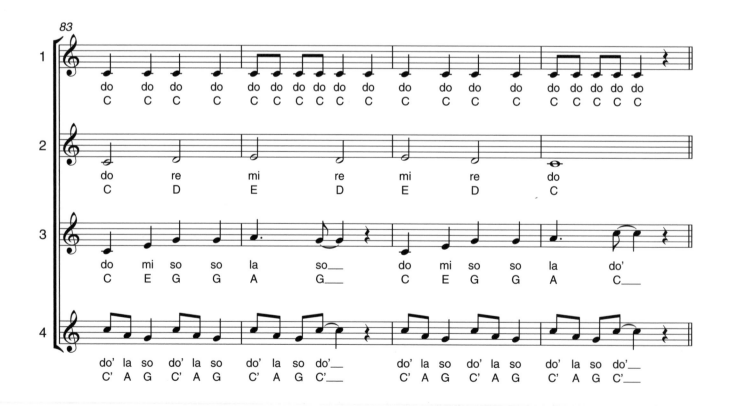

34

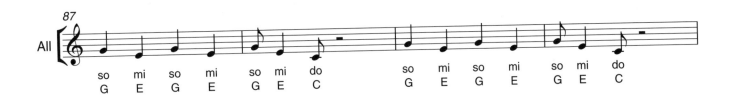

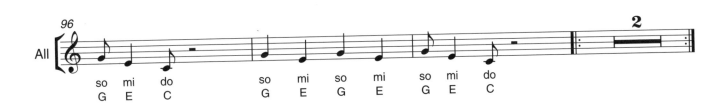

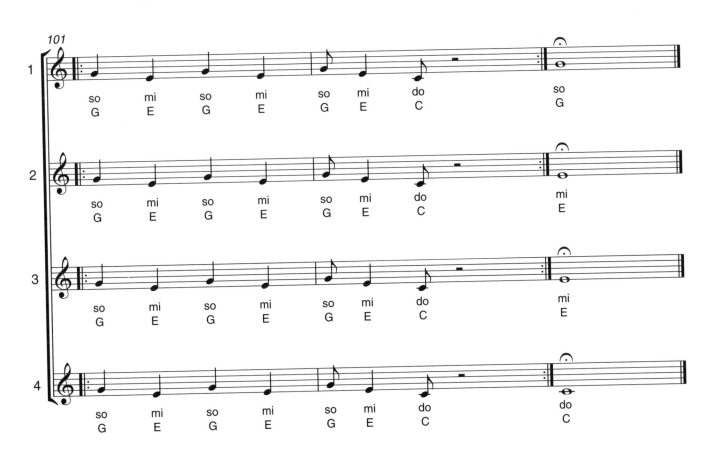

CD Listings

Recorded at Music Sales Ltd,
London W1.

1. Rocky Mountain
2. Skin and Bones
3. All Through The Night
4. So-Fa Jazz

Recorded at Swakeleys School,
Hillingdon.

5. Rocky Mountain
6. Skin and Bones
7. All Through The Night
8. So-Fa Jazz

Piano Only

9. Rocky Mountain
10. Skin and Bones
11. All Through The Night
12. So-Fa Jazz

Performers

Tracks 1 - 4

Phillipa Brothwood, Katherine Davies, Cathryn McAndrew, Kate Morgan, Jo McNally, Anna Picken,
Kaz Simmons, Clare Stevens, Imogen Trace.

Tracks 5 - 8
The Hillingdon Singers
Singers conducted and rehearsed by Jo McNally
(Please note that there may be some slight differences between this recording and the printed score)

Piano
Tracks 1-4 and 9-12: - Heather Ramage
Tracks 5-8: - Anne Torrent

1/05 (53661)